Murder Mystery Weekend

By Sheree Vickers

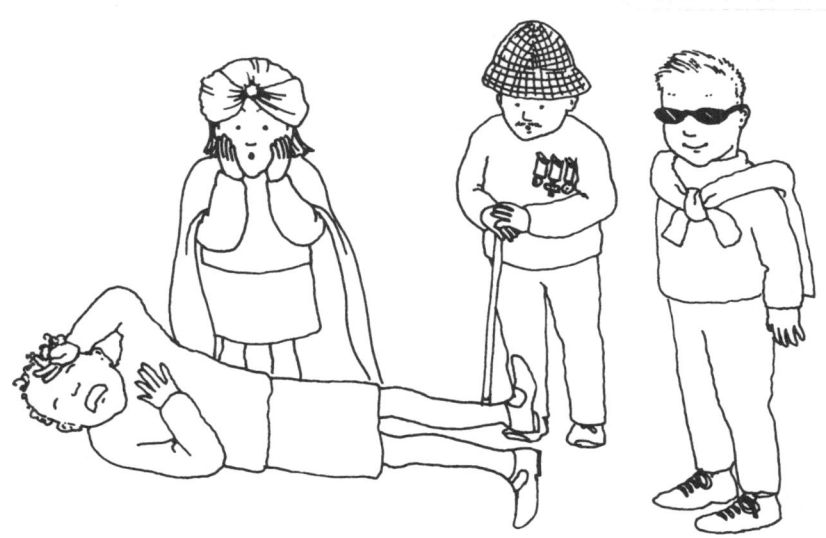

Contents

Act 1	Scene 1	3	Act 2	Scene 1	12
	Scene 2	4		Scene 2	14
	Scene 3	6		Scene 3	15
	Scene 4	7		Scene 4	16
	Scene 5	8		Scene 5	18
	Scene 6	9		Scene 6	20

Cast list

Narrator

Major Grimley Boredom

Maid

Journalist

Camera-Person

Cook

Rival Cook

Movie Star

Lovesick Fan

Repairman

Doctor

Rich Lady – Maude

Rich Man – Harold

Policeman

Detective

The Major's Niece – Jill

Madame Suzuki the Fortune Teller

Act 1
Scene 1

In the dining room of an old manor house. A large dining table with 10 chairs is set in the middle of the room.
An armchair is off to one side. Narrator enters.

Narrator: Welcome to Grimley Manor, home to Major Grimley Boredom. This is Major Boredom here.

Major Boredom is snoring very loudly in the armchair.

Narrator: We are now in the dining room, where the evening meal is about to start. Nothing has ever happened at Grimley Manor, until tonight ...

Narrator exits. Maid enters and starts to set the table.

Maid: *(Enters with a great big bored sigh)* Placemat, fork, knife, spoon. Placemat, fork, knife, spoon. Placemat, fork, knife, spoon ...

When finished she exits. Journalist and Camera-Person enter and begin to 'wire up' the room.

Journalist: Quick! Over here.

Camera Person: If I put the hidden camera here, we can cover the whole room.

Journalist: I want a secret microphone under that chair there.

Major: *(In his sleep)* Dinner!

Journalist: Quiet!

Camera Person: Hurry Up. Someone's coming.

Journalist: There. Finished.

They exit. Cook enters.

3

Cook: *(Can't make up her mind which way round they go)* Salt. Pepper. No, salt, pepper. No, salt, pepper. Right. *(Ticking off the place settings)* Vegetarian. Meat. Vegetarian. Meat. Vegetarian …

Major: Soup!

Cook: Vegetarian.

Major: Chicken!

Cook: Vegetarian.

Major: Salt.

Cook: Pepper. No, salt, pepper.

Cook exits still confused. Rival Cook enters.

Rival Cook: So, Cook thinks she is better than me at preparing the evening meal. We'll soon see about that. Sugar in the pepper pot. Pepper in the sugar pot. Salt in the salt pot. No. Pepper in the salt pot, sugar in the pepper pot and pepper in the sugar pot.

Major: Aaachooo!!!

Rival Cook: Now let's see what they think of her meal. Ha! Ha! Ha!

Rival Cook exits.

Scene 2

Movie Star enters and looks at the place settings. He is followed closely by the Lovesick Fan.

Movie Star: And WHY am I not at the head of the table? I am after all the GREATEST actor on the face of the EARTH with over 200 movies to my credit. Leading ladies swoon ...

Lovesick Fan swoons, but Movie Star does not notice.

Movie Star: dogs bark ...

Major: *(Still in his sleep)* Rrrufff!

Movie Star: ... and children weep when I appear.

Noise of weeping is heard off-stage.

Movie Star: This will never do. I'll change them myself.

Movie Star changes place settings so that he is now at the head of the table and then exits.

Lovesick Fan: Shall I compare thee to a summer's day? No. You're more like winter really. All moody and cold. But that is why I love him so. Oh! The place settings are all wrong. I must be by my love.

Lovesick Fan moves her place setting to be by the Movie Star and then exits. Repairman enters the room, looking for signs of life!

Scene 3

Repairman: Hello?

Major: *(Loud snores)*

Repairman: Is anyone here?

Major: *(Louder snores and snorts)*

Repairman: I've come about the broken chairs. *(Spies the Major asleep in the armchair)* 'Up The Hill Repairs' at your service.

Major: *(Makes a very silly noise)*

Repairman: I'll just get on with the job then.

Repairman goes under the table and begins to tinker with the dining chairs. He continues this job throughout the next scene, completely undetected by the Doctor who enters and checks Major Grimley's pulse.

Doctor: Yes, yes. Sleeping soundly – as usual.

Major: Dinner!

Doctor: *(Speaking into a tape recorder)* I really am stumped by this unusual disease. The Major is literally being bored to death. At this rate it looks like he only has about six months to live. I wish there was something I could do, but then he might as well enjoy them.

Major: What?

Doctor: I said you might as well enjoy them.

Major: Dumplings?

Doctor: Oooh! dumplings.
I might stay for dinner too.

Major: What?

Doctor:	I'm staying for dinner too.
Major:	What?
Repairman:	*(Bangs head under the table)* OW!!
Doctor:	*(To Major)* What?
Major:	Good!
Doctor:	I'll just tell Cook.

Doctor exits. Repairman comes out from underneath the table.

Repairman:	Job done! Chairs fixed! Hmm … all that talk of dumplings has made me hungry.

Repairman pulls out a place setting for himself and puts it on the table. He then exits.

Scene 4

The Rich Couple enter.

Rich Lady:	This is the place, Harold.
Rich Man:	Are you sure?
Rich Lady:	Yes, because of him *(pointing to Major)*. He's still sleeping – I hope.
Rich Man:	But what if we can't find it?
Rich Lady:	We must find it. Our whole future depends on it.
Major:	Dinner!
Rich Lady:	Why thank you. We'd love to stay. Wouldn't we, Harold?
Rich Man:	I don't know. What are they having?
Major:	Dumplings.
Rich Man:	Oooh! lovely.

Rich Lady: We'd love to stay.

Maid enters and overhears this.

Maid: Oh no. Not more people. Come with me. *(Calling off-stage)* Cook!

Maid and Rich Couple exit.

Scene 5

Policeman enters with Detective.

Policeman: The incident occurred last Tuesday when the Maid was vacuuming. She said something suspicious was lurking around the dining room and she couldn't quite put her finger on it.

Detective: I see …

Policeman: This is also the date Major Grimley's Will was read and it was discovered he would leave everything to his young niece Jill, whom he loved and adored. Rather than his nephew Jack, whom he hated and feared.

Detective: I see … and who else was present?

Policeman: Harold and Maude, Grimley's rich next-door neighbours.

Detective: I see … is that all?

Policeman:	No, Major's favourite cook, the Maid, and his favourite Movie Star.
Detective:	Why the Movie Star?
Policeman:	It is said sir, that the Movie Star will attend the opening of an envelope if invited.
Detective:	I see ... well, let's prepare for dinner and hope it's as uneventful as possible.
Policeman:	Yes, sir.

Policeman and Detective exit.

Scene 6

Jill enters with Madame Suzuki the Fortune Teller.

Jill:	*(Bounding in)* Uncle I'm home. Did you miss me? You haven't changed much. Still bored, I see. Well not to worry. I've bought home a special friend to entertain us at dinner tonight. This is Madame Suzuki, the famous Fortune Teller. She can see into the future.
Mme Suzuki:	I can feel a presence.
Jill:	Oooh!
Mme Suzuki:	Yes. All is not well at the Grimley Manor.
Jill:	Oh, isn't this exciting?

Maid enters with Cook and Rival Cook, who are arguing.

Cook:	No, the pepper's in the pepper pot.
Rival Cook:	You always add too much salt.
Cook:	I'm his favourite cook, not you.
Rival Cook:	We'll soon see about that.
Maid:	Dinner is served.

Everyone enters and takes their seat.

Jill:	Before we start, I'd like to introduce Madame Suzuki.
All:	Hello.
Jill:	Madame Suzuki, this is Maid, Cook …
Mme Suzuki:	Don't tell me. Let me guess … Cook's Arch Rival, Mr Policeman, the Detective, Maude and Harold, the Rich Couple from next door, the Repairman from 'Up The Hill Repairs', the tabloid Journalist and Camera-Person, the Famous Movie Star …
Movie Star:	*(As if accepting an award)* Well, I'd like to thank my agent, my voice coach, my pet parakeet, my mum …
All:	Sit down!

Mme Suzuki:	May I continue?
Movie Star:	By all means.
Mme Suzuki:	This is the Lovesick Fan, the family Doctor and of course, Major Grimley Boredom.
Major:	Yes!
Jill:	That's amazing. How did you know all that?
Mme Suzuki:	Easy. I read the place settings. Now, could everyone please join hands? Concentrate.

Madame Suzuki does a funny chant that everyone copies, for example:

Mme Suzuki:	Aye Aye Aye Aye Eee Eee Eee Eee I've Got a Lovely Bunch Of Coconuts *(With movements!)*

After funny chant has finished …

Mme Suzuki:	No. No, I don't believe it.
All:	What?
Mme Suzuki:	There will be a murder TONIGHT!

General GASP all round. Everyone then freezes in character.

Act 2

Scene 1

Tthe cast are on stage, as at the end of Act 1. Narrator enters.

Narrator: Told you it would be exciting. So who would die? Why would they die? How would they die and when would they die? Everyone was dying to know. Madame Suzuki could tell them nothing more except that both the murderer and the victim were currently in the room …

All: No! *(All change their frozen position.)*

Major: Yes.

Narrator: And then suddenly it happened …

Narrator exits.

Big melodramatic dying scene from Jill. Rounds of applause from everyone.

Movie Star: Bravo, darling! I couldn't have done better myself. Fabulous.

Rich Lady: That really was rather good, don't you think, Harold?

Rich Man: Oh marvellous!

Journalist: *(To Camera-Person)* Tell me you got that.

Camera Person: I got it.

Journalist: Excellent!

Maid: I suppose I'm going to have to clean it up now.

Cook: I hope it wasn't something she ate.

Rival Cook: It probably was.

Doctor: *(Checking her pulse)* Yes. She's definitely dead.

Repairman: I didn't know it was going to be Jill.

Mme Suzuki: I could have told you that.

Detective: I see …

Policeman: *(Inspecting the dead body)* Allo, allo, allo! What have we here, then?

Repairman: A dead body.

Policeman: I can see that, but what I want to know is why?

Detective: Nobody leave the room. You are all under suspicion.

Lovesick Fan: But we didn't do anything. You can't hold us against our will. How can we survive such torture? Will our strength endure? Will the pain in our hearts continue? I cannot bear this any longer.

Detective: Do you wish to leave?

Lovesick Fan: And be parted from my love – never!

Movie Star: Well I hope it won't be long. I have an audition in the morning and I don't want to be late.

Doctor: Yes, yes, and I have patients to see …

Journalist: … and I have to write a report for the newspaper …

Camera Person: … and I have to take the pictures …

Maid: … and I have to make the beds …

Repairman: … and I have to –

Policeman: *(Cutting them off)* No one is going anywhere until we can sort this murder out.

Scene 2

Detective: So tell me Cook, just what was in the salt pot?

Cook: Salt!

Rival Cook: Pepper.

Detective: I see … and what was in the pepper pot?

Cook: Pepper!

Rival Cook: Sugar.

Detective: I see … and I suppose the sugar was in the sugar pot?

Cook: Yes!

Rival Cook: No!

Detective: I see …

Policeman: *(To the maid)* And can you tell me, young Miss, just when did you set the table for dinner?

Maid: About quarter past eight. Same as I always do. Only this time more and more people kept turning up. I tell him, it's more than my job's worth but does he listen? No. He just sits in that corner and snores.

Major: *(Big snore)*

Maid: No wonder he's bored. He should try working himself for a change. I'll give him bored. Same thing, day in, day out, on and on …

Policeman: Yes, thank you Miss. I think we get the picture.

Maid: Oh really? Well I hope so. It's about time I put it on record, and another thing …

Policeman: Yes! Thank you.

Everyone's attention turns to the Movie Star.

Scene 3

Detective: I understand that your audition tomorrow is for the part of Jack The Ripper.

Movie Star: Yes it is, and it's a part I shall play brilliantly.

Policeman: Are you aware that Jack The Ripper was – A Murderer?

Movie Star: What are you implying? That I killed Jill to research the role?

Policeman: Yes.

Movie Star: I have never researched a role in my life and I certainly wouldn't start now.

Journalist: Which is precisely why you could not have killed Jill. You're not that good an actor.

Mme Suzuki: I could have told you that.

Lovesick Fan: Well I still think you're brilliant.

Scene 4

Rich Man: So it *wasn't* the Movie Star. Who else in this room is capable of murder?

Detective: How about you and your wife?

Rich Lady: Well I never. Of all the nerve. Come on Harold, we're leaving.

Rich Man: But what about – the thing?

Detective: Yes. What about – the thing?

Policeman:	I've had my eye on these two for quite some time now.
All:	Really?
Policeman:	Yes. It wasn't until the maid called me about something suspicious in this room that I put two and two together.
Major:	Four.
Policeman:	Exactly!
Rich Lady:	I knew I should have had it insured. If only Harold hadn't lost all that money at the races.
Rich Man:	Don't blame me. You're the one always spending money. Spend. Spend. Spend. That's all she ever does. If I had a penny for every cent she spent then I'd be a rich man indeed.
Maid:	Well fear not. Here it is.
Rich Lady:	My necklace!
Rich Man:	Her necklace!

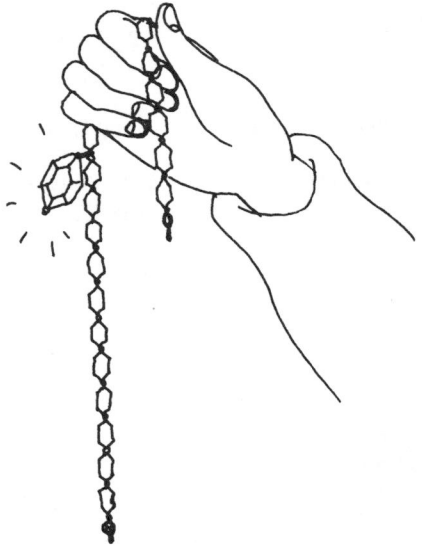

Major:	What?
All:	Her necklace!
Maid:	I found it in the vacuum cleaner.
Rich Lady:	Oh thank you. How can we ever make it up to you?
Maid:	You could give me a job. I'm bored out of my head with this one.
Rich Man:	You're hired. You start in the morning. My socks need ironing and the beds need making and the dog needs walking and the silver needs polishing and …

Scene 5

Doctor:	Yes, yes, that's all very well, but could we please get on with finding out who the murderer is?
Repairman:	Well, what about you? As the family Doctor, you always had access to the house.
Policeman:	Very true.
Doctor:	I have taken a Hippopotamus Oath. I would hardly try to kill anyone, now would I?

Detective:	Exactly! Much like the Policeman and myself, we are here to uphold the law, not break it.
Policeman:	Very true.
Doctor:	You can't just go around accusing people. There must be proof.
Journalist:	That's where *we* can come in. For exclusive rights to the story I can now reveal that the murderer has been caught on our hidden surveillance camera.
All:	What?
Camera Person:	Using the latest technology I was able to wire a miniature camera into the bottom of this salt pot.
Cook:	Pepper pot.
Rival Cook:	Sugar pot.
All:	Sshh!!!!

Camera Person:	So, if you would all just sign these exclusive documents giving us the copyright to a million-pound fortune on the sale of these tapes, I can then let you see who the murderer is.
Movie Star:	Wait a minute. I'm on those tapes too, you know. I demand that my agent be informed.
Lovesick Fan:	Yes.
Movie Star:	And my publicist.
Lovesick Fan:	Yes.
Movie Star:	And my mum.
Lovesick Fan:	What?
Movie Star:	My mum.
Lovesick Fan:	But what about me? For years I've been following you, just hoping you'd notice me. Notice how dedicated I am to you. And now that your 'Big Break' has finally arrived, who do you contact? Your mum!
Journalist:	*(To Lovesick Fan)* We could give you a 36-week in-depth pull-out Sunday supplement describing in detail your spurned love affair with the now famous Movie Star.
Camera Person:	And I could take the pictures.
Lovesick Fan:	Sold!

Scene 6

Doctor:	Yes, yes, that's all very well, but we still haven't discovered who the murderer is.
Policeman:	It's all a simple process of elimination …

Detective: Harold and Maude we know are innocent because all they wanted was the necklace.

Harold: Yes.

Maude: Absolutely.

Policeman: Neither of the cooks could have killed Jill because she hadn't eaten anything at the time.

Cook: I told you so.

Rival Cook: No, I told *you* so.

Maid: Well it certainly wasn't me.

Detective: You're right. When you set the table, what did you place down?

Maid: *(In the same bored manner)* Placemat, fork, knife, spoon. Placemat, fork, knife, spoon. Placemat, fork, knife, spoon …

Detective: Exactly! Jill was not killed with cutlery.

Policeman: And *why* were the Journalist and Camera-Person 'wiring up the room'? Perhaps they knew of a murder about to take place?

Journalist: Never!

Camera Person: Absolutely not!

Detective: Then why *were* you 'wiring up the room'? Trying to catch pictures of people in their underwear to print in the Sunday paper?

Journalist: Yes.

Camera Person: Maybe.

Doctor: So, how does that leave us?

Mme Suzuki: In our underwear?

Policeman: No. It leaves us with …

Detective: The Repairman!

All: The Repairman?

Major: What?

All: The Repairman.

Detective: … who isn't a Repairman at all. He is in fact *(going over to Repairman and taking off his cap)* Jack – Major Grimley's nephew, whom he hated and feared.

Everyone:	Jack?!
Mme Suzuki:	I could have told you that.
Repairman:	Yes, me. If Jill died I would inherit Grimley Manor. I know Uncle hated and feared me, but I'm not that bad really. What's a little murder between friends, hey?
Doctor:	I've known you since you were a little boy. How could you do such a thing?
Repairman:	Quite easily, really. You see, I wired Jill's chair so that when she reached for the pepper pot ...
Cook:	Salt pot.
Rival Cook:	Sugar pot.
All:	Sshh!!!!
Repairman:	The electric shock created such an impact that it killed her.
Policeman:	Well Jack, I'm arresting you for the murder of your sister Jill.
Repairman:	And I would have got away with it too, if it weren't for you pesky kids!

Everyone freezes except the Major, who is still sleeping.
Narrator enters.

Narrator: Well that's the end of our play. Jack, alias The Repairman, went to prison. The Journalist and Camera-Person won international acclaim for their coverage of the event, the Movie Star was never heard from again, the Lovesick Fan is now a household name, the Maid got even more bored at Harold and Maude's house next door and the doctor finally managed to find a cure for the Major's boredom – he married him off to Madame Suzuki!

THE END